Pond Dipping

Sweep the net through the water,
then tip your catch into a jar.
Now take a look.
Newts or fishes?
Beetles? A squishy mass of eggs?
Wiggly worms or things with lots of legs?
Maybe you can work out what they are
or maybe not.
The lovely thing with pond dipping
is just looking.
And when you're done – gently pour them back.

Lambs' Tails

Lambs' tails wiggle when they're happy.
A wiggle, wiggle, squiggle
That shows just how they feel.

You'll see it happen when a lamb is feeding.
It butts its mum and starts to suck,
Then watch the tail go!

All over the fields in spring,
Lambs' tails are wiggling.
You see them and you want to smile.

FIVE REASONS TO KEEP CHICKENS

1. They look very silly when they are taking a dust bath.

2. They perch in the funniest places.

3. They will eat the caterpillars on your vegetables, and chase flies (which is very funny).

4. The cockerel looks so sweet when he roosts with his wings around his hens.

5. Collecting eggs when they are still warm from under the hen is wonderful.

Summer Song

In the city park at sunrise,
a little brown bird sings,
"Tu-loo, tu-loo, tu-loo,
chuck, chuck, weeeeeeeee!"
His song says "this tree is mine!"

At midday in the hot, dry grass,
a cricket rubs a leg along his wing,
"Chirr chirr, chirr chirr, chirr chirr!"
His song says "come and be my mate!"

In the pond at midnight,

the frog's throat puffs up to call,

"Rrrruuup, rrrruuup,

rrruuup, rrruuuuup!"

His song says "I'm the biggest!"

Everywhere you go, just listen:

someone's always singing.

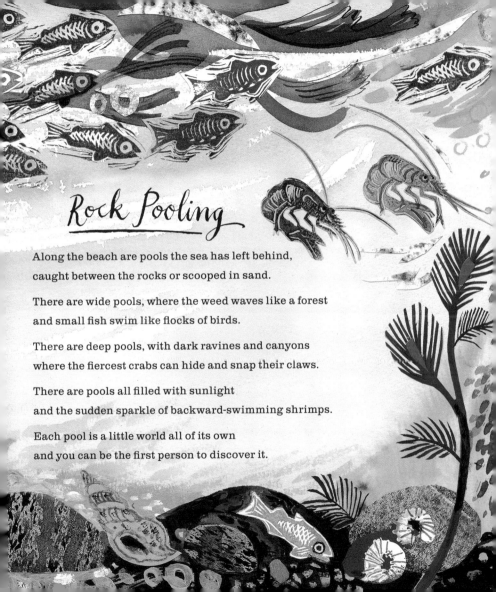

Rock Pooling

Along the beach are pools the sea has left behind,
caught between the rocks or scooped in sand.

There are wide pools, where the weed waves like a forest
and small fish swim like flocks of birds.

There are deep pools, with dark ravines and canyons
where the fiercest crabs can hide and snap their claws.

There are pools all filled with sunlight
and the sudden sparkle of backward-swimming shrimps.

Each pool is a little world all of its own
and you can be the first person to discover it.

Moth

Phuttt! Phutttt!

Something's battering the light bulb,

fluttering and fussing.

It has wings just like a butterfly,

but when it rests

it folds them flat across its back.

It's a moth.

It flies at night

and steers by the moon's glow.

It got muddled by the lamplight,

so it flew indoors.

Switch off the light

and leave the window open.

It will fly off safe into the dark.

Patchwork Pigeons

Patchwork pigeons, made of sky,
Catch the rain clouds when they fly.

Just Ducks

The moment that they see you're going to feed them,

the ducks come hurrying across the pond,

as if you'd pulled them by a string.

First two or three, then ten, then even more.

There are drakes, the boy ducks, with the brightest colours,

and girl ducks, with their quiet streaks of brown.

There are ducks that like to dive, and those that dabble.

All of them, together, feasting, squabbling,

splashing silver drops of water on their feathery backs.

Lizard

Quick as a blink.
What was it?
Fast as thinking –
There, then not there.
Quick as a blink.

Quick as a blink.
Eyes glinting,
Tail whipping,
Tongue flicking.

It's a lizard!
Quick as a blink.